GREAT MINDS® WIT & WISDOM

Grade 6 Module 3:
Narrating the Unknown

Mashaер 604

Student Edition

COPYRIGHT STATEMENT

Table of Contents

Name _____

Date _____ Class _____

Handout 1A: Optional Fluency Practice 1

Directions:

1. Day 1: Read the text carefully and annotate to help you read fluently.
2. Each day:
   a. Practice reading the text three to five times.
   b. Evaluate your progress by placing a checkmark in the appropriate, unshaded box.
   c. Ask someone (adult or peer) to listen and evaluate you as well.
3. Last day: Respond to the self-reflection questions.

In the time of the first planting of corn

there will come a tribe from the bay of the Chesapeake.

This tribe will build their longhouses on the land of the

    Powhatan.

They will hunt and fish and plant on the land of the

    Powhatan.

Three times the Powhatan will rise up against this tribe.

The first battle will end and the Powhatan will be

    victorious.

But the tribe will grow strong again.

The Powhatan will rise up.

The second battle will end and the Powhatan will be

    victorious.

But the tribe will grow strong once more.

The third battle will be long and filled with bloodshed.

By the end of this battle, the Powhatan kingdom

    will be no more.

Carbone, Elisa. *Blood on the River: James Town 1607*. Puffin Books, 2006, p. 1.

Name _____

Date _____ Class _____

Student Performance Checklist:ᶠ	Day 1		Day 2		Day 3		Day 4	
	You	Listener*	You	Listener*	You	Listener*	You	Listener*
Accurately read the passage 3–5 times.								
Read with appropriate phrasing and pausing.								
Read with appropriate expression.								
Read articulately at a good pace and an audible volume.								

*Adult or peer

Self-reflection: What choices did you make when deciding how to read this passage, and why? What would you like to improve on or try differently next time? (*Thoughtfully answer these questions below.*)

Name _____

Date _____   Class _____

Handout 3A: Plot and Character Development

Directions: Create the following table in your Response Journal for your group's assigned chapters. Chapter 1 has been completed for you as a model.

- **Plot Development:** Choose a main event from the chapter that contributes to the story line. Briefly summarize the event and explain how it helps move the plot forward.

- **Character Development:** Explain how a character responds and/or changes because of his involvement in this main event and why this character development is significant.

Note: In order to showcase your understanding of how a key event advances the plot, you may include questions that a reader might ponder after an event occurs. These questions should capture how an event needs some type of closure or resolution.

Chapter	Plot Development:	Character Development:
1	Samuel gets caught by the shopkeeper the following morning after stealing his mother's locket. Conflict is created when Samuel gets caught and fights with the shopkeeper and his son. The reader does not know what will happen to Samuel now. Will he go to jail? Will his head be stuck on a pole at London Bridge?	Although Samuel unsuccessfully fights against the shopkeeper and his son, he does not stop trying to fight for what is right in his mind. When the son grabs onto him, he "[throws] his head back hard" to try to get away (Carbone 5). He shows how determined and brave he is by retaking his mother's locket no matter the cost (which is a blow to his head and possibly a trip to the gallows). Samuel shows the reader that he is a fighter by nature. He fights against unfairness and what is corrupt. The reader can tell there is more fight left in him, and we wonder what he will fight against next.
4	Captain Smith Being Arrested (23)	Captain Smith was fuming But he was ABle do Control his emotions
5	Captain smith was crying & shirking in the woods they see Red wells & Hatchit	Captain Ratcliff used his knowledge to Burn the swords Down.

Name _____

Date _____ Class _____

Handout 5A: Factor Tracker

Directions: Use this table to track the social and environmental factors (both negative and positive) that impact the new colony of Jamestown as you read *Blood on the River* and the other module texts. Add the text and page numbers, then sort and explain the factor, and indicate whether it positively (+) or negatively (−) impacts Jamestown's development. Continue your Factor Tracker in your Response Journal when you run out of space (hint: keep this handout in your Response Journal).

- **Social factors** are causes that come from people. They include how people treat each other and behave towards each other.

- **Environmental factors** are causes that come from the natural world. They are not made by humans; environmental factors exist in nature.

Text/page number	Social Factor	Environmental Factor
	the Indians keep on Attacking the colonists outside of Jamestown the gentlemen are still not helping	the men are to sick to work (−)

Name

Date   Class

Text/page number	Social Factor	Environmental Factor
	Smith has left for the orient & the men stopped Working Rely school	
	The gentleman have stolen All the Food Jamestown e HAVE takn it on the Ship Capt. Smith	

Name _____

Date _____ Class _____

Handout 5B: Optional Fluency Practice 2

Directions:
1. Day 1: Read the text carefully and annotate to help you read fluently.
2. Each day:
   a. Practice reading the text three to five times.
   b. Evaluate your progress by placing a checkmark in the appropriate, unshaded box.
   c. Ask someone (adult or peer) to listen and evaluate you as well.
3. Last day: Respond to the self-reflection questions.

One day Captain Smith surprises us. "I believe the savages are spying on us," he says. "I have watched the way they look around while they are here. I think they are counting our men, seeing where our tents are located, and plotting an attack. We have invaded their land, and I believe they will fight us to get it back. We must build a palisade to protect the settlement."

"Nonsense," declares President Wingfield. "You see how friendly they are. If we build a palisade it will look as if we are enemies. We will build no fortification."

Captain Smith grumbles, but there is no arguing with President Wingfield. And I think that President Wingfield is right; the Indians have been very friendly and welcoming to us.

Carbone, Elisa. *Blood on the River: James Town 1607*. Puffin Books, 2006, p. 72.

Student Performance Checklist:	Day 1		Day 2		Day 3		Day 4	
	You	Listener*	You	Listener*	You	Listener*	You	Listener*
Accurately read the passage 3–5 times.								
Read with appropriate phrasing and pausing.								
Read with appropriate expression.								
Read articulately at a good pace and an audible volume.								

*Adult or peer

Name

Date   Class

Self-reflection: What choices did you make when deciding how to read this passage, and why? What would you like to improve on or try differently next time? (*Thoughtfully answer these questions below.*)

Name _____

Date _____   Class _____

Handout 5C: Experiment with Pronoun Number

Directions: Read the paragraph below. Consider whether a singular or plural pronoun belongs in each blank space before writing in the one that agrees with its corresponding noun.

Captain Smith finds me and hands _____ a straw hat and a hatchet and

tells _____ to get to work. We will begin felling the smaller trees in order to make

room for our tents and gardens. James and Richard are assigned to work alongside me. My

inclination is to work on _____ own and ignore _____. But would it be so

bad to work with _____, _____ wonder, to cooperate? Better than being

chained up by Captain Smith again with no slop bucket nearby. I decide to give it a try.

I see that it would be best to have one boy bend a sapling over, another boy chop

_____ at its base with strong downward strokes, and the third boy drag the

saplings into a brush pile. I clear my throat, "Do _____ want to work together on

this?" I ask _____. I explain my idea (Carbone 68–69).

Name _____

Date _____   Class _____

Handout 6A: Evidence Collection

Directions: Are words more powerful than weapons for the Jamestown settlers like Smith suggests, or are weapons more powerful than words?

Listen carefully as the examples of evidence provided in the table below are explained. Then, skim the text and collect additional evidence for both sides to help you determine your claim. Share your ideas with the class! Write down ideas from your peers!

Weapons are more powerful than words for the settlers.	Words are more powerful than weapons for the settlers.
Captain Gosnold points out that the expedition team would have been killed by the Indians "if it had not been for the cannons scaring them off" (83). This expedition team had Smith with them as a translator, but it did not help. They needed weapons, more than words, to survive.	The gentlemen unshackle Smith because he is the only one, they believe, who can translate for them. Smith's understanding of the Algonquian language helps him regain power on board the ship and saves his life.
When the Indians mount an attack on Jamestown, the only reason why the Indians leave "in retreat" is because someone begins firing the cannons (79). Before the attack, the settlers were communicating with the Indians, and they thought they were on good terms, but the Indians were tricking them. The only reason why the settlers survive is because the settlers' weapons are more powerful than the Indians' weapons. Words don't help in this situation.	Captain Smith has Samuel study the Algonquian language. He knows that if Samuel learns this language, he will be valued by the settlers and the Indians. He will become an important person to each group because he will be able to help people communicate. This position will bring him power.

Name

Date   Class

Weapons are more powerful than words for the settlers.	Words are more powerful than weapons for the settlers.

Name _____

Date _____ Class _____

Handout 7A: Evidence Collection

Directions: Should Captain Smith or Reverend Hunt be Jamestown's next president?

Review the text and <u>collect evidence</u> for your group's assigned candidate. When the class reconvenes and shares findings, record evidence for the other candidate, so that you can then determine your claim.

Captain Smith for President!	Reverend Hunt for President!

Name _____

Date _____   Class _____

Handout 7B: Samuel's Perspective of Factors Threatening Jamestown

Directions: For each negative social or environmental factor identified in the first column, explain Samuel's perspective about this factor and its threat to Jamestown's survival. Leave the third column blank; you will complete this column for Lesson 8.

Negative Factor Impacting Jamestown	Samuel's Point of View	Carbone's Word Choice That Conveys Samuel's Perspective
Social: The conflict with the Powhatans		
Social: The conflict between the commoners and the gentlemen		
Social: The conflict among the boys		
Environmental/Social: A constant lack of food and supplies		
Environmental: Disease and illness		

Name

Date   Class

Handout 7C: Frayer Model

Directions: Use a dictionary, the text, and discussion with your group members to complete this Frayer Model.

Definition of *clamoring*:

Characteristics of something that is *clamoring*:

Word:

clamoring

Examples:
(What kind of things *clamor*?
How do people react to that type of noise?)

Non-Examples:
(What makes sound but doesn't *clamor*? How do people feel about these sources of noise?)

Name _____

Date _____   Class _____

Handout 8A: Explanatory Essay Graphic Organizers

Directions: You may use these optional graphic organizers to help you plan your explanatory essay.

Introduction
Hook
Introduce
Thesis & Preview

Name _____

Date _____   Class _____

Supporting Paragraph

Topic Statement:

Evidence:

Citation:

Elaboration:

Evidence:

Citation:

Elaboration:

Concluding Statement:

Name _____

Date _____ Class _____

Conclusion

Name _____

Date _____ Class _____

Handout 9A: Speaking and Listening Checklist

Directions: Evaluate your participation by marking + for "yes" and Δ for "needs improvement" in the appropriate boxes. Ask someone (adult or peer) to evaluate your participation as well.

Grade 6 Speaking and Listening Checklist			
	Self +/ Δ	Peer +/ Δ	Teacher +/ Δ
I used text evidence to support my opinion.			
I asked questions.			
I responded to questions.			
I made relevant observations.			
I followed all the rules for speaking in a group.			
I set and met my participation goal.			
I acknowledged and elaborated on comments from my peers.			
I listened to interpret when engaging with my peers.			
I understood my peers' points.			
I built off my peers' points.			
I stayed engaged in the conversation the whole time.			
I brought the conversation back on topic when needed.			
I used appropriate, formal, academic language. For example:			
I used vocabulary that I learned in this module, such as these words:			

Name

Date   Class

1. What is your goal for today's Socratic Seminar to improve your participation?

_____

_____

2. Did you meet your goal? Why or why not?

_____

_____

3. What will your goal be for the next discussion?

_____

_____

Name _____

Date _____ Class _____

Socratic Seminar Sentence Starters

Statements and Questions	For Clarification or Paraphrasing
▪ I wonder why... ▪ What if we looked at this in a different way, such as... ▪ What in the text makes you say that? ▪ How does that support our idea about... ▪ In my mind I see... ▪ Based on..., I infer that... ▪ Do you agree or disagree with... ▪ I am still confused by... ▪ Based on..., I predict that...	▪ Could you please rephrase that? ▪ Can you say more about that? ▪ I have a question about that... ▪ Could someone please paraphrase that? ▪ In other words, are you saying... ?
For Building Ideas	**For Different Viewpoint**
▪ I agree with ___ and I'd like to add... ▪ I really like that idea because... ▪ That idea is important because... ▪ If we change that a little, we can see... ▪ Another example of ___ is... ▪ This reminds me of... ▪ Now I am wondering... ▪ This relates back to our essential question because...	▪ That's a great point, but I think... ▪ I agree with the part about ___ , but I think... ▪ On the other hand, what about... ▪ The evidence seems to suggest something different, such as... ▪ I politely disagree with ___ because...
Partners	**Problem-Solving**
▪ We decided that... ▪ During the Think-Pair-Share, ___ pointed out to me that... ▪ After our Think-Pair-Share, I believe I have a new idea... ▪ We concluded that...	▪ I think the way to continue is... ▪ We should identify... ▪ I think we should do this step by step starting with... ▪ Another way to look at this is... ▪ I feel like we are missing something because... ▪ Maybe we can reframe this by... ▪ Which thinking map could we use to help us?
Summarizing	Other
▪ I'd like to go back to what ___ was saying and... ▪ So, the big idea is... ▪ So, what can we conclude from this? ▪ After our analysis, it appears that... ▪ Several things contributed to this conclusion; the most important was...	▪ ▪ ▪ ▪ ▪

Name _____

Date _____ Class _____

Handout 10A: Pronoun Experiment

Directions: The paragraph below was written without pronouns. Read it aloud quietly and consider how incorporating pronouns could improve this paragraph. With your partner, rewrite the paragraph, ensuring that any pronouns use appropriate number and person.

Samuel and Namontack work together to build a house and Samuel and Namontack talk while building the house. Samuel is getting better at understanding Namontack's language so Samuel understands when Namontack tells Samuel that the houses built by Namontack's people are better than the houses built by Samuel's people. Namontack says the houses built by Namontack's people are built from thin saplings and the thin saplings are bound together with woven mats. Namontack says this makes the houses of Namontack's people warmer than the houses of Samuel's people. Samuel tries to imagine Namontack's village and hopes Samuel can see a village like Namontack's someday (adapted from Carbone 139).

_____

_____

_____

_____

_____

_____

_____

_____

_____

_____

_____

_____

_____

Name _____

Date _____ Class _____

Handout 11A: Reasons, Evidence, and Elaboration

Directions: For the first paragraph, note how the reason, evidence, and elaboration have been identified: the reason is underlined, the evidence is numbered, and the elaboration is starred. Working with your partner, reread the claim and then read the second paragraph. Afterward, underline the reason, number the evidence, and star any sentences that provide elaboration.

Identification Code:

- **Underline Reason**
- **Number Evidence**
- **Star Elaboration**

Claim: Samuel should live with the Native Americans before returning to Jamestown because it will benefit the settlement.

Paragraph #1:

Samuel should stay on at Werewocomoco because he can learn the Algonquian language and in the future help communicate with the Indians on behalf of the settlers. (1) For example, Samuel knows that if he becomes fluent in Algonquian, he would be able "to trade and help the colony" (163). * Samuel has already seen Smith prove multiple times that knowing the Indians' language results in the two groups finding a way to communicate their trading needs. * There have been many times when the settlers have almost starved because of bad crop harvests or other issues, and Smith's ability to speak Algonquian and trade with the Indians has saved the settlers' lives. (2) In addition, besides helping out with trading, having a colonist who speaks the Algonquian language has helped the settlers learn vital information. For example, when a friendly group of Indians visits the settlement, Smith is able to translate, and he learns from them "that [the settlers] should cut down the tall grass near [the] fort because that is where [the settlers'] enemies are hiding when they shoot [them]" (103). * This information helps save settlers' lives. (3) Finally, Smith goes on expeditions, and the settlement needs an extra translator while he is gone, which Samuel could be. * When Smith has been gone in the past, the settlers have found themselves without enough food and no one to negotiate deals with the Indians. * Having an extra translator would ensure that the colonists can communicate their needs to their neighbors. The settlers' lives will only improve if Samuel spends time with the Indians and returns to Jamestown fluent in Algonquian.

Name _____

Date _____ Class _____

Paragraph #2:

      Samuel should also live with the Indians because they will teach him indispensable skills and impart valuable knowledge that he can rely upon to help the settlers. For example, if Samuel spends time with the Native Americans, he can learn how to make "a bow and arrows and to shoot straight" (163). Learning these skills would help Samuel be able to hunt and feed himself and others. In the past, the settlers have run out of food, or they have been rationed "one cup of grain for each person each day," which leaves them constantly "hungry" (174). They cannot rely always on the Indians to trade or bring them food because their relationship with the Native Americans is strained. If Samuel learns how to properly hunt, he can help the settlement by increasing their food supply, enriching their diet by getting them more protein, and making them not so dependent on the Indians for survival. Also, if Samuel learns how to make bows and arrows, he can teach others back at Jamestown how to make these important weapons that can also be used for defense, since the Virginia Company has not given everyone a gun. The settlement would benefit from these extra weapons because many Indian tribes continue to attack them. In addition, by living with the Native Americans, Samuel can continue to learn how best to grow food. Namontack has already taught him how to plant corn and beans "so that the bean plants can climb the cornstalks" and get enough light to grow (145). Samuel and the settlers do not know the plants of the New World, but the Indians do, and their knowledge about how to cultivate and harvest New World crops is invaluable. Samuel can use this knowledge to improve the settlers' gardening techniques, and instead of plants growing poorly, the settlement can enjoy better harvests. The skills and knowledge Samuel will acquire by living with the Native Americans will help the settlers survive the challenges of the New World.

Name

Date   Class

Handout 12A: Frayer Model

Directions: Use a dictionary, the text, and discussion with your group members to complete this Frayer Model.

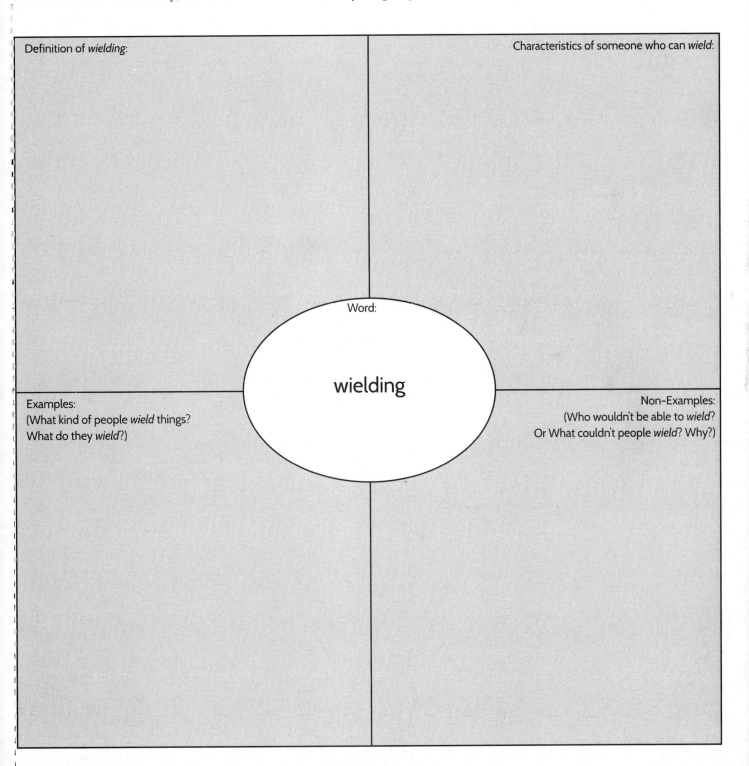

Definition of *wielding*:

Characteristics of someone who can *wield*:

Word:

wielding

Examples:
(What kind of people *wield* things?
What do they *wield*?)

Non-Examples:
(Who wouldn't be able to *wield*?
Or What couldn't people *wield*? Why?)

Name _____

Date _____   Class _____

Handout 13A: Experiment with Reasons, Evidence, and Elaboration

Directions: As a class, we will read the prompt and claim, and next identify the first paragraph's components (the reason, evidence, and elaboration). Afterward, working with your partner, complete the following steps:

1   Read the preselected evidence that could be used to create a second reason that supports the claim;

2   Draft this second reason;

3   Decide which two pieces of evidence most effectively support your reason;

4   Draft the remaining paragraph by inserting your reason and adding in evidence and elaboration. For elaboration, make sure to explain how the evidence supports the paragraph's reason and the overall claim.

Prompt: Should Samuel kidnap baby Virginia and take her to Point Comfort, or does she have a better chance of survival at Jamestown?

Claim: Samuel should kidnap baby Virginia because she has a better chance of survival at Point Comfort than Jamestown.

Paragraph #1:

Samuel should kidnap baby Virginia because living at Jamestown is dangerous due to two factors that could prove fatal for a baby. First, the new settlers "have attacked Indian villages and made enemies where [they] used to have friends" (197). These Indians have been cruelly and wrongly treated. The "jewels from the bodies of their dead werowances" have been stolen and their houses have been set on fire (190). Samuel knows that the peace Smith makes after this disaster "cannot last" because "there has been too much killing" (194). The likelihood that the Indians will attack Jamestown–like they have many times in the past–is great. If an Indian attack occurs, a little baby stands no chance of surviving, especially given the Indians cruel treatment of enemies they have captured in the past, like George Cassen a former settler the Indians killed by burning him alive. Second, at Jamestown there are "too many settlers to feed, and yet hardly anyone is working to store food for the winter" (197). Samuel has lived a few winters at Jamestown when starvation has occurred, and he knows that no food means many deaths. In addition, if the Indians regard the settlers as their enemy, there is little chance that the Jamestown colonists can trade for food, and they won't have Smith or Samuel there to negotiate. A baby is especially helpless. If she doesn't eat–or Ann cannot produce enough milk because she is starving–she will die. Therefore, baby Virginia should not stay at Jamestown during this particular winter, due to the increased Indian conflict and the decrease in food supplies.

Name

Date   Class

Paragraph #2:

Read the following preselected evidence and consider how it could be used to generate a second reason supporting the claim:

- Samuel will be living at Point Comfort.
- Samuel has deep friendships with certain Indians who live across the river from Point Comfort.
- Samuel has Captain Smith's "new world diamonds" and speaks Algonquian (201).
- There will only be "about thirty men to feed" at Point Comfort (205).
- There is "artillery" at Point Comfort (205).
- Point Comfort will have its "own hogs, fish to catch, and oysters to dig" (205).

(Reason #2) Samuel should also kidnap baby Virginia because:

_____

_____

_____

Then choose the two best pieces of evidence from the collection above and provide elaboration about how this evidence supports the reason and the claim.

_____

_____

_____

_____

_____

_____

_____

Name _____

Date _____ Class _____

Handout 13B: Optional Fluency Practice 3

Directions:

1. Day 1: Read the text carefully and annotate to help you read fluently.
2. Each day:
   a. Practice reading the text three to five times.
   b. Evaluate your progress by placing a checkmark in the appropriate, unshaded box.
   c. Ask someone (adult or peer) to listen and evaluate you as well.
3. Last day: Respond to the self-reflection questions.

What shall I say? But thus we lost him, that in all his proceedings, made justice his first guide, and experience his second; ever hating baseness, sloth, pride, and indignitie, more than any dangers; that never allowed more for himselfe, then his soldiers with him; that upon no danger would send them where he would not lead them himselfe; that would never see us want what either he had, or could by any means get us…whose adventures were our lives, and whose losse our deathes.

Carbone, Elisa. *Blood on the River: James Town 1607*. Puffin Books, 2006, p. 200.

Student Performance Checklist:	Day 1		Day 2		Day 3		Day 4	
	You	Listener*	You	Listener*	You	Listener*	You	Listener*
Accurately read the passage 3–5 times.								
Read with appropriate phrasing and pausing.								
Read with appropriate expression.								
Read articulately at a good pace and an audible volume.								

*Adult or peer

Self-reflection: What choices did you make when deciding how to read this passage, and why? What would you like to improve on or try differently next time? (*Thoughtfully answer these questions on the back of this paper.*)

Name _____

Date _____   Class _____

Handout 14A: Samuel's Letter to Captain Smith

Directions: Pretend you are Samuel, and you sit down one winter evening and write a letter to Captain Smith informing him about what has taken place since his departure. In your letter, make sure you cover the following events and moments of *Blood on the River* using descriptive language:

1. The <u>climax of the novel</u>: when you anxiously await punishment for kidnapping baby Virginia and learn of Ratcliffe's execution;

2. and the <u>resolution</u>: when your sentence of twenty lashings is retracted and you create a happy and safe existence for yourself at Point Comfort living with John Laydon's family.

Stay true to what you know about Samuel as you capture his voice and retell these events. Keep in mind that the audience is Captain Smith, so include details that you know Samuel would share with this particular character.

Name _____

Date _____ Class _____

Handout 15A: Argumentative Essay Graphic Organizers

Directions: You may use these optional graphic organizers to help you plan your argumentative essay.

Introduction
Hook
Introduce
Claim and Preview

Name

Date   Class

Supporting Paragraph	
Reason:	
Evidence: Citation:	**Elaboration:**
Evidence: Citation:	**Elaboration:**
Concluding Statement:	

You are not limited to two pieces of evidence/elaboration for each reason. Add additional as needed to fully support your reason.

Name

Date   Class

Conclusion

Name

Date   Class

Handout 16A: Challenges of Writing Historical Fiction

Directions: While reading the Author's Note, use this handout to record notes that you can later use to complete the New-Read Assessment.

1. Identify three challenges Carbone faced while writing *Blood on the River*.

2. Explain why each issue was a challenge.

3. Explain how Carbone responded to and solved that challenge.

Author's Note		
Challenge	**Why**	**Solution**

Name _____

Date _____ Class _____

Handout 16B: "Address to Captain John Smith," Chief Powhatan

Directions: Read Chief Powhatan's historical speech delivered to Captain John Smith in 1609. Next, reread the speech, and jot down the main idea of each paragraph. Underline words or phrases that support what you identify as the gist.

1   I am now grown old, and must soon die; and the succession must descend, in order, to my brothers,

2   Opitchapan, Opekankanough, and Catataugh, and then to my two sisters, and their two daughters.

3   I wish their experience was equal to mine; and that your love to us might not be less than ours to you.

4   Why should you take by force that from us which you can have by love? Why should you destroy us, who

5   have provided you with food? What can you get by war? We can hide our provisions, and fly into the

6   woods; and then you must consequently famish by wronging your friends.

7   What is the cause of your jealousy? You see us unarmed, and willing to supply your wants, if you will come in

8   a friendly manner, and not with swords and guns, as to invade an enemy. I am not so simple, as not to know

9   it is better to eat good meat, lie well, and sleep quietly with my women and children; to laugh and be

10   merry with the English; and, being their friend, to have copper, hatchets, and whatever else I want, than to

11   fly from all, to lie cold in the woods, feed upon acorns, roots, and such trash, and to be so hunted, that I

12   cannot rest, eat, or sleep. In such circumstances, my men must watch, and if a twig should but break, all

13   would cry out, "Here comes Captain Smith"; and so, in this miserable manner, to end my miserable life;

14   and, Capt. Smith, this might be soon your fate too, through your rashness and unadvisedness.

15   I, therefore, exhort you to peaceable councils; and, above all, I insist that the guns and swords, the cause of

16   all our jealousy and uneasiness, be removed and sent away.

Powhatan. Address to Captain John Smith. *Biography and History of the Indians of North America*, written by Samuel G. Drake, 3rd edition, O.L. Perkins, 1834, book IV, pp. 11–12. Google Books, digitized by Google, 4 Dec. 2006, Web. Accessed 29 Aug. 2017.

Name

Date   Class

Handout 17A: Optional Fluency Practice 4

Directions:
1. Day 1: Read the text carefully and annotate to help you read fluently.
2. Each day:
   a. Practice reading the text three to five times.
   b. Evaluate your progress by placing a checkmark in the appropriate, unshaded box.
   c. Ask someone (adult or peer) to listen and evaluate you as well.
3. Last day: Respond to the self-reflection questions.

I am now grown old, and must soon die; and the succession must descend, in order, to my brothers, Opitchapan, Opekankanough and Catataugh, and then to my two sisters, and their two daughters.

I wish their experience was equal to mine; and that your love to us might not be less than ours to you. Why should you take by force that from us which you can have by love? Why should you destroy us, who have provided you with food? What can you get by war? We can hide our provisions, and fly into the woods; and then you must consequently famish by wronging your friends.

What is the cause of your jealousy? You see us unarmed, and willing to supply your wants, if you come in a friendly manner, and not with swords and guns, as to invade an enemy. I am not so simple, as not to know it is better to eat good meat, lie well, and sleep quietly with my women and children; to laugh and be merry with the English; and, being their friend, to have copper, hatchets, and whatever else I want, than to fly from all, to lie cold in the woods, feed upon acorns, roots, and such trash, and to be so hunted, that I cannot rest, eat, or sleep. In such circumstances, my men must, and if a twig should but break, all would cry out "Here comes Capt. Smith"; and so, in this miserable manner, to end my miserable life; and, Capt. Smith, this might be soon your fate too, through your rashness and unadvisedness.

I, therefore, exhort you to peaceable councils; and, above all, I insist that the guns and swords, the cause of all our jealousy and uneasiness, be removed and sent away.

Powhatan. Address to Captain John Smith. *Biography and History of the Indians of North America*, written by Samuel G. Drake, 3rd edition, O.L. Perkins, 1834, book IV, pp. 11–12. Google Books, digitized by Google, 4 Dec. 2006, Web. Accessed 29 Aug. 2017.

Name

Date   Class

Student Performance Checklist:	Day 1		Day 2		Day 3		Day 4	
	You	Listener*	You	Listener*	You	Listener*	You	Listener*
Accurately read the passage 3–5 times.								
Read with appropriate phrasing and pausing.								
Read with appropriate expression.								
Read articulately at a good pace and an audible volume.								

*Adult or peer

Self-reflection: What choices did you make when deciding how to read this passage, and why? What would you like to improve on or try differently next time? (*Thoughtfully answer these questions below.*)

Name _____

Date _____   Class _____

Handout 18A: Argumentative Essay Writing Model

Directions: Read Read the following model essay that answers Focusing Question Task 2 (which you completed in Lesson 15). Review the argumentative essay outline found on the next page. Then complete the following steps:

1   In the **introduction**, underline the essay's claim and number its supporting reasons.

2   For each **supporting paragraph**, circle transitional words and phrases; place a check next to evidence; and a question mark next to each sentence containing elaboration (indicating that the elaboration helps answer questions in the reader's mind about how the evidence supports both the reason and the claim).

3   In the **conclusion**, underline any words or phrases that reinforce the essay's argument.

Introduction: It is not often that risky and desperate behavior is rewarded with new opportunities. When Samuel reaches the orphanage, he is angry. He's been arrested for theft. He'd rather fight others rather than risk trusting anyone. For these reasons, he's chosen to be John Smith's page on the journey to Virginia, which changes Samuel's life. John Smith has the greatest impact on Samuel's growth and change while living in Jamestown. Because of Smith, Samuel learns how to channel his anger and he understands that people must work together to survive in the New World.

Supporting Paragraph 1: Samuel begins his journey angry and ready to fight. Instead, John Smith shows Samuel how to calm himself down and use his anger as motivation. Smith tells Samuel to "*Channel* it—let it give [him] the strength for what [he] can do to change things, to make things better" (201). This advice helps Samuel see that managing his anger is a way create positive change. Smith's advice is especially impactful because Samuel sees Smith using the same strategy, "[he has] watched [Smith] do this over and over, this shifting of anger into calm action" (201). Seeing Smith channel his anger makes it easier for Samuel to understand how to do so himself. This allows Samuel to grow as a person. Without this Smith's intervention, Samuel would have continued to have angry outbursts. He might have even been arrested again. He never would have gained his freedom without Smith's help. John Smith truly changed Samuel's life.

Supporting Paragraph 2: Besides managing his anger, John Smith teaches Samuel that he must work with others to survive. Before coming to Jamestown, Samuel's philosophy is "Trust no one" (17). He believes he can survive without anyone's help. John Smith helps Samuel understand that existing this way in the New World isn't an option because, "The wilderness is like a ship in a storm. [They] need one another to survive" (56). John Smith forces Samuel to depend on others. He even sends him to live with the Warraskoyacks where he learns skills that will help all the settlers in Virginia survive. Smith creates opportunities for Samuel to work alongside others instead of against them. Had Smith not intervened, Samuel would have been alone. Once Samuel has learned this important lesson, Smith frees him from his servitude. Learning this lesson from John Smith radically changes Samuel's path.

Conclusion: John Smith's impact on Samuel is life-altering. If Samuel continued to get violently angry or refuse to work with others in James Town, his behavior might have cost him his life. Instead, John Smith's influence helps Samuel earn his freedom and find a family in which he belongs. All of the things Samuel wished for in England have come true in Virginia because of the impactful influence of John Smith.

Name

Date   Class

Argumentative Essay Outline and Components

H	Hook	Catch your audience's attention.	
I	Introduce	Introduce your audience to the topic.	
C	**Claim**	State your claim(s) about the topic,	
		and preview your	supporting reasons.

R	**Reason**	State a reason that supports your claim.	
E	Evidence	Cite evidence for the reason, including necessary context.	
E	**Elaboration**	Explain how the evidence relates to the reason.	
C	**Concluding Statement**	Close the paragraph.	

R	**Reason**	Transition from your last reason, and	state another reason that supports your claim.
E	Evidence	Cite evidence for the reason, including necessary context.	
E	**Elaboration**	Explain how the evidence relates to the reason.	
C	**Concluding Statement**	Close the paragraph.	

C	Conclusion	Reinforce your argument, reflecting on its significance.	

Name _____

Date _____ Class _____

Handout 19A: Introduction and Conclusion Practice

Directions: Draft either an introduction or conclusion with your partner for the incomplete essay found below. Reference Handout 18A: Argumentative Essay Writing Model and review its outline if needed.

Question: What is one of the novel's big ideas that captures Samuel's <u>best</u> response to the unknowns of Jamestown?

Claim: Samuel's best response to the unknowns of Jamestown is choosing the path of love and not of fear.

Intro:

_____

_____

_____

_____

_____

_____

_____

_____

_____

_____

_____

Supporting Paragraph 1: Survival in Jamestown is a big unknown that Samuel confronts by choosing to become friends and cooperate with his fellow settlers. Before coming to the New World, Samuel does not believe that he is "teachable," and he rejects people's help and friendship (9). His motto is "trust no one," for he believes that people will only disappoint or abuse him (17). In the New World where survival is not guaranteed, he begins to see that his philosophy of pushing people away does not work. Captain Smith opens Samuel's mind to the idea that the colonists "will need one another to survive" (56). Samuel begins to believe in the "importance of standing together, or cooperating" and making his "circle" of support "bigger" (136). He becomes friends with Richard, whose friendship helps him deal with Reverend Hunt's death and helps him not feel alone when Captain Smith is not at Jamestown. He also cooperates more willingly, like when he works tirelessly and successfully to put out the fire that threatens Jamestown. By embracing and cooperating with other people, Samuel not only gains friends and protection, but he also allows himself to learn from others and develop his abilities, which contribute to his survival in an unknown land.

Name _____

Date _____ Class _____

Supporting Paragraph 2: Samuel also responds with an open heart and mind to the Native Americans, a people who are unfamiliar and unknown to him. When Samuel meets Namontack, he willingly learns from him and does not become angry or upset when Namontack informs Samuel that the Indian way of life is superior to that of the settlers. Samuel reacts to Namontack in this way because he recognizes that building a friendly relationship with the Indians "means survival and peace" (141). In addition, while living with the Warraskoyacks, he seeks their friendship and their guidance. Kainta teaches him how to make arrows and kill prey with the weapons Samuel makes, and he continues to learn Algonquian. Samuel begins to view himself as capable and "strong" because of the new skills he has acquired by allowing others to teach him (183). He knows that "with the knowledge (he has) gained from living with the Warraskoyacks, (he doesn't) ever have to be hungry again" (185). These changes in Samuel are important because he has a better chance of surviving in the New World if he values the knowledge and skills others can share with him.

Conclusion:

_____

_____

_____

_____

_____

_____

_____

_____

_____

_____

Name _____

Date _____ Class _____

Handout 19B: Chief Powhatan's Perspective

Directions: Skim again Chief Powhatan's "Address to Captain John Smith" (Handout 16B), and then determine Powhatan's perspective about the settlers and the Native Americans as it is conveyed through his use of language. Then analyze how events and characters on *Blood on the River* support his perspective <u>or</u> call it into question.

Note: This handout is to help you draft a response to Focusing Question Task 3. You do not need to use complete sentences when you record notes on this handout.

Chief Powhatan's Perspective: what is it, and how does language help convey it?	How do events and characters in *Blood on the River* support Powhatan's perspective?	How do events and characters in *Blood on the River* contradict Powhatan's perspective?
	The settlers	

Name

Date   Class

How do events and characters in *Blood on the River* contradict Powhatan's perspective?	How do events and characters in *Blood on the River* support Powhatan's perspective?	Chief Powhatan's Perspective: what is it, and how does language help convey it?
		The Native Americans

Name _____

Date _____ Class _____

Handout 20A: Reliability and Credibility of Sources

Directions: Follow the directions below to assess the credibility and reliability of your sources.

Part 1: Find at least two sources (based on the criteria covered during the lesson) that are reliable and credible in supplying

List these sources here:

1) Source 1: Explain why this source is both *reliable* and *credible*.

_____

_____

_____

2) Source 2: Explain why this source is both *reliable* and *credible*.

_____

_____

_____

Part 2: Please complete notes for the following questions about your subject (person, place, thing, or event), using at least two sources as references. In your notes, make sure to cite from which source you obtained the information.

1) <u>What</u> is your subject?

_____

2) <u>Where?</u> For example, where did this person live? Where did this event take place?

_____

_____

3) <u>When?</u> What dates might be important to record for your person, place, thing, or event?

_____

_____

Name _____

Date _____ Class _____

4) <u>Why?</u> Why is this person, place, thing, or event important historically? Why is it/are they important to study?

_____

_____

_____

_____

_____

_____

5) <u>How</u> did this person, place, thing, or event contribute to the decline or development of Jamestown and/or the English colony?

_____

_____

_____

_____

_____

_____

_____

_____

Name _____

Date _____ Class _____

Handout 21A: "Rethinking Jamestown," Jeffery Sheler

Directions: Use this article as directed in this and upcoming lessons. To help you as you read, work with, and discuss the text, lines have been numbered on the left side and paragraphs have been numbered on the right side.

1 America's first permanent colonists have long been considered incompetent. But new evidence suggests	
2 that it was a drought–not indolence–that almost did them in.	
3 To the english voyagers who waded ashore at the mouth of the Chesapeake Bay on a balmy April day in 1607, the	
4 lush Virginia landscape must have seemed like a garden paradise after four and a half months at sea. One ebullient	
5 adventurer later wrote that he was "almost ravished" by the sight of the freshwater streams and "faire meddowes	
6 and goodly tall trees" they encountered when they first landed at Cape Henry. After skirmishing with a band	1
7 of Natives and planting a cross, the men of the Virginia Company expedition returned to their ships–the Susan	
8 Constant , Godspeed and Discovery – and the 104 passengers and crew continued up the Powhatan River (soon to	
9 be renamed the James in honor of their King, James I) in search of a more secure site.	
10 They thought they had found it on a marshy peninsula some 50 miles upstream–a spot they believed could be	
11 defended against Indians attacking from the mainland and that was far enough from the coast to ensure ample	
12 warning of approaching Spanish warships. They set about building a fortress and clearing land for the commercial	2
13 outpost they had been sent to establish and which they called "James Cittie." They were eager to get down to the	
14 business of extracting gold, timber and other commodities to ship back to London.	
15 But Jamestown proved to be neither paradise nor gold mine. In the heat of that first summer at the mosquito-	
16 infested settlement, 46 of the colonists died of fever, starvation or Indian arrows. By year's end, only 38 remained.	
17 Were it not for the timely arrival of British supply ships in January 1608, and again the following October,	3
18 Jamestown, like Roanoke a few years before, almost certainly would have vanished.	
19 It is little wonder that history has not smiled on the colonists of Jamestown. Though recognized as the first	
20 permanent English settlement in North America and the setting for the charming (if apocryphal) tale of Pocahontas	
21 and Capt. John Smith, Jamestown has been largely ignored in colonial lore in favor of Massachusetts' Plymouth	
22 Colony. And what has survived is not flattering, especially when compared with the image of industrious and devout	
23 Pilgrims seeking religious freedom in a new land. In contrast, the Jamestown settlers are largely remembered as a	4
24 motley assortment of inept and indolent English gentlemen who came looking for easy money and instead found	
25 self-inflicted catastrophe. "Without a trace of foresight or enterprise," wrote historian W. E. Woodward in his 1936 A	
26 New American History , " . . . they wandered about, looking over the country, and dreaming of gold mines."	
27 But today the banks of the James River are yielding secrets hidden for nearly 400 years that seem to tell a different	
28 story. Archaeologists working at the settlement site have turned up what they consider dramatic evidence that the	
29 colonists were not ill-prepared dandies and laggards, and that the disaster-plagued Virginia Colony, perhaps more	5
30 than Plymouth, was the seedbed of the American nation–a bold experiment in democracy, perseverance and	
31 enterprise.	

Name

Date   Class

32   The breakthrough came in 1996, when a team of archaeologists working for the Association for the Preservation
33   of Virginia Antiquities (APVA) discovered a portion of the decayed ruins of the original 1607 Jamestown fort, a
34   triangular wooden structure many historians were certain had been swallowed by the river long ago. By the end
35   of the 2003 digging season, the archaeologists had located the fort's entire perimeter on the open western edge
36   of the heavily wooded 1,500-acre island; only one corner of it had been lost to the river. "This was a huge find,"
37   William Kelso, chief archaeologist at the site, said shortly after the discovery. "Now we know where the heart is,
38   the center of the colonial effort, the bull's-eye. We know exactly where to dig now, and we will focus our time and
39   resources on uncovering and analyzing the interior of the James Fort."

6

40   Since then, Kelso and his team have excavated the ruins of several buildings inside the fort's perimeter, along with
41   thousands of artifacts and the skeletal remains of some of the first settlers.

7

42   Only a third of the site has been excavated, and many of the artifacts are still being analyzed. Yet the evidence
43   has already caused historians to reconsider some longheld assumptions about the men and the circumstances
44   surrounding what YaleUniversity history professor emeritus Edmund S. Morgan once called "the Jamestown fiasco
45   ." "Archaeology is giving us a much more concrete picture of what it was like to live there," says Morgan, whose 1975
46   history, American Slavery, American Freedom: The Ordeal of Colonial Virginia , argued that Jamestown's first years
47   were disastrous. "But whether it turns the Virginia Company into a success story is another question."

8

48   The large number of artifacts suggests that, if nothing else, the Virginia Company expedition was much better
49   equipped than previously thought. By the end of the 2003 season, more than half a million items, from fishhooks
50   and weaponry to glassmaking and woodworking equipment, along with the bones of game fish and assorted
51   livestock, had been recovered and cataloged. Many are now on display at the Jamestown Rediscovery project
52   headquarters, a clapboard Colonial-style building a few hundred yards from the fort. "All of this flies in the face of
53   conventional wisdom, which says that the colonists were underfunded and illequipped, that they didn't have the
54   means to survive, let alone prosper," says Kelso. "What we have found here suggests that just isn't the case."

9

55   In a climate-controlled room down the hall from Kelso's sparsely decorated office, Beverly Straube, the project's
56   curator, sorts and analyzes the detritus of everyday life and death in the Virginia Colony. Some of the more
57   significant artifacts are nestled in shallow open boxes, labeled and carefully arranged on long tables according to
58   where the items were found. From one box, Straube picks up a broken ceramic piece with drops of shiny white
59   "frosting" attached to its surface. "It's part of a crucible," she explains. "And this," she says, pointing to the white
60   substance, "is molten glass. We know from John Smith's records that German glassmakers were brought in to
61   manufacture glass to sell back in London. Here we have evidence of the glassmakers at work in the Jamestown
62   fort." From another box, she takes a broken ceramic piece with a cut-out hole and an ear-like protrusion. She
63   compares it with a sketch of a ceramic oven, about the size of a toaster, used by 16th-century craftsmen to make
64   clay tobacco pipes. Nearby are fragments of a glass alembic (a domed vessel used in distilling) and a ceramic boiling
65   vessel, known as a cucurbit, for refining precious metals. "These artifacts tell us that the colonists weren't just sitting
66   around," Straube says. "When they were healthy enough to work, this was an industrious place."

10

67   In another room, Straube opens a drawer and pulls out a pitted piece of iron–round, with a point protruding from
68   its center. It is a buckler, she explains, a shield used in hand-to-hand combat. It was found in a trench surrounding
69   the fort's east bulwark. By 1607, she says, bucklers were considered largely obsolete as tools of war in Europe–which
70   would seem to fit the traditional view that the Jamestown expedition was provisioned with castoff weapons and
71   equipment. "But we believe these were deliberately chosen," Straube says, "because the settlers knew they were
72   more likely to face guerrilla-type combat against Indian axes and arrows than a conventional war against Spanish
73   firearms. So the buckler would have come in handy."

11

Name

Date   Class

74   In the cellar of what had been a mud-walled building that extends outward from the eastern palisade wall,
75   archaeologists have found pottery shards, broken dishes and tobacco pipes, food remains, musket balls, buttons
76   and coins. The cellar had been filled with trash, probably in 1610 during a massive cleanup of the site ordered by the
77   newly appointed governor, Lord de la Warre, who arrived at Jamestown just in time to prevent the starving colonists   12
78   from abandoning the settlement and returning to England. Establishing the date helps show that the cellar's
79   contents, which included the glassmaking and distilling equipment on display at the APVA headquarters, dated to
80   the colony's critical first years. It is from such early artifacts that Kelso and Straube are revising the colony's history.

81   Sifting through cellars and trenches in and around the fort, Kelso and his team recently uncovered a surprisingly
82   large quantity of Indian pottery, arrowheads and other items. These suggest that the colonists had extensive
83   dealings with the Natives. In one cellar, an Indian cooking pot containing pieces of turtle shell was found next to
84   a large glass bead that the English used in trade with the Indians. "Here we believe we have evidence of an Indian   13
85   woman, inside the fort, cooking for an English gentleman," Straube says. While such arrangements may have
86   been rare, Kelso adds, the find strongly implies that Natives occasionally were present inside the fort for peaceful
87   purposes and may even have cohabited with the Englishmen before English women arrived in significant numbers
88   in 1620.

89   What is known from Virginia Company papers is that the colonists were instructed to cultivate a close relationship
90   with the Indians. Both documentary and archaeological records confirm that English copper and glass goods   14
91   were exchanged for Indian corn and other foods, initially at least. But the relationship didn't last long, and the
92   consequences for both the English and the Indians proved deadly.

93   As grim as the first year was at Jamestown, the darkest days for the colonists were yet to come. In 1608, the
94   settlement was resupplied twice with new recruits and fresh provisions from London. But when nearly 400 new
95   immigrants arrived aboard seven English supply ships in August 1609, they found the colonists struggling to survive.
96   In September, the former president of the colony, John Ratcliffe, led a group of 50 men up the PamunkeyRiver   15
97   to meet with Wahunsunacock–better known as Chief Powhatan, the powerful leader of the Powhatan Indians–to
98   bargain for food. The colonists were ambushed, Ratcliffe was taken prisoner and tortured to death, and only 16 of
99   his men made it back to the fort alive (and empty handed).

100   That fall and winter in Jamestown would be remembered as "the starving time." Out of food, the colonists grew sick
101   and weak. Few had the strength to venture from their mudand- timber barracks to hunt, fish or forage for edible
102   plants or potable water. Those who did risked being picked off by Indians waiting outside the fort for nature to   16
103   take its course. Desperate, the survivors ate their dogs and horses, then rats and other vermin, and eventually the
104   corpses of their comrades. By spring, only 60 colonists were still alive, down from 500 the previous fall.

105   The starving time is represented by debris found in a barracks cellar–the bones of a horse bearing butchery marks,
106   and the skeletal remains of a black rat, a dog and a cat. To the west of the fort, a potters' field of hastily dug graves–
107   some as early as 1610–contained 72 settlers, some of the bodies piled haphazardly on top of others in 63 separate   17
108   burials.

109   In the conventional view of Jamestown, the horror of the starving time dramatizes the fatal flaws in the planning
110   and conduct of the settlement. Why, after three growing seasons, were the men of Jamestown still unable or
111   unwilling to sustain themselves? History's judgment, once again, has been to blame "gentlemen" colonists who
112   were more interested in pursuing profits than in tilling the soil. While the Virginia "woods rustled with game and   18
113   the river flopped with fish," according to The American Pageant, a 1956 history textbook, the "soft-handed English
114   gentlemen . . . wasted valuable time seeking gold when they should have been hoeing corn." They were "spurred to
115   their frantic search" by greedy company directors in London who "threatened to abandon the colonists if they did
116   not strike it rich."

Name

_____

Date   Class

_____

117   But Kelso and Straube are convinced the fate of the colony was beyond the control of either the settlers or their
118   London backers. According to a landmark 1998 climate study, Jamestown was founded at the height of a previously
119   undocumented drought—the worst seven-year dry spell in nearly 800 years. The conclusion was based on a tree-
120   ring analysis of cypress trees in the region showing that their growth was severely stunted between 1606 and 1612.
121   The study's authors say a major drought would have dried up fresh-water supplies and devastated corn crops on
122   which both the colonists and the Indians depended. It also would have aggravated relations with the Powhatans,
123   who found themselves competing with the English for a dwindling food supply. In fact, the period coincides
124   perfectly with bloody battles between the Indians and the English. Relations improved when the drought subsided.

19

125   The drought theory makes new sense of written comments by Smith and others, often overlooked by historians. In
126   1608, for example, Smith records an unsuccessful attempt to trade goods for corn with the Indians. "(Their corne
127   being that year bad) they complained extreamly of their owne wants," Smith wrote. On another occasion, an Indian
128   leader appealed to him "to pray to my God for raine, for their Gods would not send any." Historians have long
129   assumed that the Powhatans were trying to mislead the colonists in order to conserve their own food supplies. But
130   now, says archaeologist Dennis Blanton, a co-author of the tree-ring study, "for the first time it becomes clear that
131   Indian reports of food shortages were not deceptive strategies but probably true appraisals of the strain placed on
132   them from feeding two populations in the midst of drought."

20

133   Blanton and his colleagues conclude that the Jamestown colonists probably have been unfairly criticized "for poor
134   planning, poor support, and a startling indifference to their own subsistence." The Jamestown settlers "had the
135   monumental bad luck to arrive in April 1607," the authors wrote. "Even the best planned and supported colony
136   would have been supremely challenged" under such conditions.

21

137   Kelso and his co-workers are hardly the first archaeologists to probe the settlement. In 1893, the APVA acquired
138   22.5 acres of JamestownIsland, most of which had become farmland. In 1901, the U.S. Army Corps of Engineers
139   constructed a sea wall to protect the site from further river erosion; a few graves and the statehouse at the
140   settlement's western end were excavated at the time as well. In the 1950s, National Park Service archaeologists
141   found footings and foundations of 17th-century structures east of the fort and hundreds of artifacts, though they
142   couldn't locate the fort itself; since the 1800s it was widely assumed to lie underwater.

22

143   Today, the site of the original colonial settlement is largely given over to archaeological research, with few visual
144   links to the past. Kelso and a full-time staff of ten work almost year-round, and they're assisted by some 20
145   student workers during the summer. Tourists wander the grassy site snapping pictures of Kelso's team toiling behind
146   protective fences. Bronze statues of Smith and Pocahontas stand along the James River. There's a gift shop and a
147   restored 17th-century church. And a $5 million "archaearium"—a 7,500-square-foot educational building that will
148   house many of the colonial artifacts— is to be completed for the 2007 quadricentennial.

23

149   The surge in research at the original Jamestown can be traced to 1994, when the APVA , anticipating the colony's
150   400th anniversary, launched a ten-year hunt for physical evidence of Jamestown's origins and hired Kelso, who had
151   excavated 17th-century sites near Williamsburg and was then conducting historical research at Monticello.

24

152   Kelso is unmistakably pleased with the revisionist spin his findings have given to the Jamestown saga. Yet rewriting
153   history, he says, was not what he had in mind when he began the work. "I simply wanted to get the rest of the story,"
154   he says. Most of what is known of Jamestown's grim early years, he notes, comes from the writings of Smith—clearly
155   the most prolific of the colony's chroniclers—and a handful of his compatriots, along with a few sketchy records from
156   the Virginia Company in London. Such documents, Kelso says, are a "deliberate record" and often are "written with a
157   slant favorable to the writer." Smith's journal, for example, frequently depicts many of his fellow colonists as shiftless
158   and inept. But Smith's journal "is obviously slanted," says Kelso. "He comes out the star in his own movie."

25

Name _____

Date _____ Class _____

159   An example is the tale of Smith's rescue by the Indian princess Pocahontas, which Smith first related in his writings
160   in 1624, some 17 years after the incident. Because the story was never mentioned in his earlier writings, some
161   historians now dismiss it as legend—though Pocahontas did exist.   26

162   Not that Jamestown's archaeological evidence is beyond question. Some archaeologists argue that it's nearly
163   impossible to date Jamestown's artifacts or differentiate the founding colonists' debris from what later arrivals
164   left behind. Retired Virginia archaeologist Ivor Noël Hume, the former director of archaeology at nearby Colonial   27
165   Williamsburg, notes that the fort was occupied until the 1620s and was rebuilt several times. "It's hard to pin down
166   what the original settlers brought with them and what came later," he says.

167   But Kelso and Straube say they can accurately date most of the artifacts and draw reasonable conclusions as to
168   when certain structures were built and abandoned. "If we find a piece of broken pottery in a trash pit, and another
169   piece of the same vessel in a nearby well," Straube explains, "we know these two structures existed at the same   28
170   time." Moreover, she says, the appearance of certain imported items from Portugal, Spain or Germany indicate
171   a period after the Virginia Company lost its charter in 1624 and the colony's management was turned over to
172   England's Crown. "It's really a different Jamestown in the later period," she says.

173   Some historians still have their doubts. "What they are finding may require some adjustment to the views of
174   historians relying solely on documents," Yale's Morgan concedes. But the reputation of Jamestown as a failure will be   29
175   a hard one to shake, he adds: "It will take a lot more than a half million artifacts to show that the Virginia Company
176   learned from its mistakes and made a go of it in the colonies."

177   Kelso is convinced that much more colonial history lies buried in the island's soil. During the 2004 digging season,
178   excavators uncovered the footprint of a long and narrow building inside the fort. The presence of unusually fancy
179   glassware and pieces of Chinese porcelain buried inside suggests to Straube that it was a place of high-style dining   30
180   and entertaining, perhaps the governor's home, which written records indicate was built in 1611. In the cellar of
181   another structure, a student volunteer uncovered wine bottles, intact but empty, that are believed to date to the late
182   1600s, when Jamestown was prospering as a tobacco and trade center.

183   "Were there gentlemen at Jamestown?" says Kelso. "Of course. And some of them were lazy and incompetent.
184   But not all. The proof of the matter is that the settlement survived, and it survived because people persisted and
185   sacrificed." And what began as an English settlement gradually evolved into something different, something new.   31
186   "You look up and down the river as the settlement expanded and you find it is not like England. The houses are
187   different—the towns, the agriculture, the commerce. They were really laying the roots of American society." Despite
188   the agony, the tragedy, and all of the missteps, says Kelso, "this is where modern America began."

Sheler, Jeffery L. "Rethinking Jamestown." *Smithsonian Magazine*, Smithsonian Institution, Jan. 2005. Web. Accessed
15 Sept. 2016.

Name

Date   Class

Handout 21B: "Rethinking Jamestown" Summary

Directions: Reread Sheler's "Rethinking Jamestown" (Handout 21A) and stop after each paragraph to create a one sentence summary of what you've just read.

Paragraph	Summary
1	
2	Colonists found a secure location and began building their settlement.
3	
4	
5	
6	
7	
8	
9	Artifacts excavated from the remains of Jamestown show that colonists were working and manufacturing things.
10	
11	Colonists had bucklers to protect them from Indian attacks.
12	Kelso and Straube analyze artifacts from a trash site to better understand the colonists' lives.
13	
14	

Name _____

Date _____   Class _____

Paragraph	Summary
15	By September of 1609, many new colonists had arrived and an attempt to trade with the Powhatans led to an ambush and attack.
16	The fall and winter of 1609 was called "the starving time;" people got sick and ate their pets and the dead bodies of others.
17	Remains at the Jamestown site show the devastation of the starving time.
18	Many historians blame the starving time on lazy, greedy gentlemen who weren't willing to work hard enough to sustain the Jamestown colony.
19	
20	
21	
22	Other archaeologists have tried to excavate the Jamestown site but it was believed that it was under water.
23	The Jamestown site is still being excavated today and also has buildings and displays for visitors.
24	People became more interested in finding Jamestown before the 400th anniversary of the settlement.
25	
26	Although Pocahontas was real, the story about her saving John Smith is untrue.
27	Some archeologists question whether it's possible to determine when artifacts were used or brought to Jamestown.
28	Kelso and Straube believe that they can accurately date the artifacts based on where they were found or originated.
29	
30	Kelso and Straube are still making new discoveries at the site.
31	

Name _____

Date _____ Class _____

Handout 21C: Word Relationships

Directions: Read the excerpt from Sheler's article, with particular attention to the relationships between each word pair. Then answer the questions below.

> The study's authors say a major drought would have dried up fresh-water supplies and devastated corn crops on which both the colonists and the Indians depended. It also would have <u>aggravated</u> <u>relations</u> with the Powhatans, who found themselves competing with the English for the <u>dwindling</u> food supply … Relations improved when the drought subsided (Sheler 164–170).

1. What is the relationship between *aggravated* and *relations*?

_____

_____

_____

2. What is the relationship between *relations* and *dwindling*?

_____

_____

_____

3. What is the relationship between *aggravated* and *dwindling*?

_____

_____

_____

Name _____

Date _____ Class _____

Handout 22A: Mapping an Argument

Directions: Reread Sheler's "Rethinking Jamestown" (Handout 21A) and map Sheler's argument using the table below. Be sure to paraphrase and reference all with the line numbers from the text. Use as many reason boxes and as many evidence rows as necessary.

Claim

Reason

Evidence

Name

Date   Class

Reason

Evidence

Evaluation
How effective is Sheler's use of reasons and evidence in supporting his claim about Jamestown? Are his reasons logical? Is his evidence and elaboration credible and sufficient?

Name

Date   Class

Handout 25A: Boxes and Bullets Organizer–Chapter 1

Directions: Add the supporting details for each section's given main idea in the Boxes and Bullets Organizer below. Then use the main ideas and details to write a summary of the chapter.

Text: Chapter 1, *Written in Bone*
Main Idea of page 9: Historians and scientists have always been interested in the lives and deaths of Jamestown settlers.
Details: -   -   -   -
Main Idea of pages 14–15: The rediscovery of James Fort was very complex.
Details: -   -   -   -

Name

Date   Class

Main Idea of pages 16–17:
Soil features proved that the remains of Jamestown had been found

Details:

-

-

-

-

Main Idea of "Under the Soil" on pages 19–21:
Archaeologists follow specific procedures when looking for graves in the soil.

Details:

-

-

-

-

Summary of chapter 1:

Name

Date   Class

Handout 26A: Boxes and Bullets Organizer–Chapter 2

Directions: Add the supporting details for each section's given main idea in the Boxes and Bullets Organizer below. Then use the main ideas and details to write a summary of the chapter.

Text: Chapter 2, *Written in Bone*
Main Idea of pages 22–24:
Details: -   -   -   -
Main Idea of "How Old Were You?" on pages 27–30:
Details: -   -   -   -

Name

Date   Class

Main Idea of "He or She?" on pages 30–32:

Details:

-

-

-

-

Main Idea of "Where Did You Come From?" on pages 32–35:

Details:

-

-

-

-

Summary of chapter 2:

Name _____

Date _____ Class _____

Handout 27A: Photograph Analysis

Directions: Choose one of the following photographs from chapters 1 and 2 of *Written in Bone* and complete the steps below. You'll notice these are the same steps we followed when we studied Hopper's painting, *Nighthawks*. Although it may be difficult, please ignore the surrounding text and the captions (cover them with sticky notes if you're tempted) and focus solely on your selected photograph.

Step 1: Notice and Wonder
Look at the photograph for several minutes and record your observations and questions.

Notice	Wonder

Step 2: Organize Ideas
Carefully observe the photograph again, this time noting what you see for each of the following categories.

Setting	People	Objects

Colors	Textures	Other

Name

Date   Class

Step 3: Build Inferences

Use their objective observations and develop at least three inferences about what you are seeing in the photograph. Help each other revise any inferences built on judgment or subjectivity.

Step 4: Synthesize Understanding

Finally, given all you have noticed and thought about, how does this photograph help us build understanding about the discoveries at the Jamestown site?

Be prepared to share your findings with the whole group.

Name _____

Date _____ Class _____

Handout 28A: Boxes and Bullets Organizer–Chapter 3

Directions: Use this optional Boxes and Bullets Organizer as needed to support you in writing the summary of chapter 3 as part of New-Read Assessment 2.

Text: Chapter 3, *Written in Bone*
Main Idea of _____
Details: ▪   ▪   ▪   ▪
Main Idea of _____
Details: ▪   ▪   ▪   ▪

Name _____

Date _____   Class _____

Main Idea of _____

Details:

- ·

- ·

- ·

- ·

Main Idea of _____

Details:

- ·

- ·

- ·

- ·

Name

Date   Class

Handout 28B: Experiment with Sentence Variety

Directions: Read the excerpt on the left from Powhatan's speech. Rewrite Powhatan's ideas on the right, incorporating more sentence variety to engage reader interest.

I am not so simple, as not to know it is better to eat good meat, lie well, and sleep quietly with my women and children; to laugh and be merry with the English; and, being their friend, to have copper, hatchets, and whatever else I want, than to fly from all, to lie cold in the woods, feed upon acorns, roots, and such trash, and to be so hunted, that I cannot rest, eat, or sleep (Powhatan, 8-12).	

Name

Date   Class

Handout 29A: Boxes and Bullets Organizer–Chapter 4

Directions: Add the main idea and supporting details for each section in Boxes and Bullets Organizer below. Then use the main ideas and details to write a summary of the chapter.

Text: Chapter 4, *Written in Bone*
Main Idea of pages 44–45 (stop after second full paragraph):
Details: ■   ■   ■   ■
Main Idea of pages 45–46 (stop after second full paragraph):
Details: ■   ■   ■   ■

Name

Date   Class

Main Idea of pages 48–50 (start at second full paragraph on 48 and stop after second full paragraph on 50):
Details:
▪
▪
▪
▪
Main Idea of pages 50–52:
Details:
▪
▪
▪
▪
Summary:

Name _____

Date _____ Class _____

Handout 30A: Sheler and Carbone

Directions: Complete the provided Venn diagram to compare and contrast the following two excerpts from Sheler's "Rethinking Jamestown" and Carbone's *Blood on the River*. If you need help, review the Venn diagram completed as a class in Lesson 27 with two other excerpts from these texts.

"After skirmishing with a band of Natives and planting a cross, the men of the Virginia Company expedition returned to their ships–the Susan Constant, Godspeed, and Discovery–and the 104 passengers and crew continued up the Powhatan River" (Sheler 1).

At dusk we hear voices and look out to see the men returning. They are in good spirits, and I wonder if they've found gold already. ... Suddenly I hear a cry, then frantic shouting and someone moaning. I run to the railing. In the half-light of dusk I see them, five of them, crouched on a hill, their naked bodies painted, arrows flying from their longbows ... A gentlemen, Gabriel Archer, has been shot through both hands, and a sailor has been shot twice in the torso (Carbone 61–62).

Name

Date   Class

CARBONE

SHELER

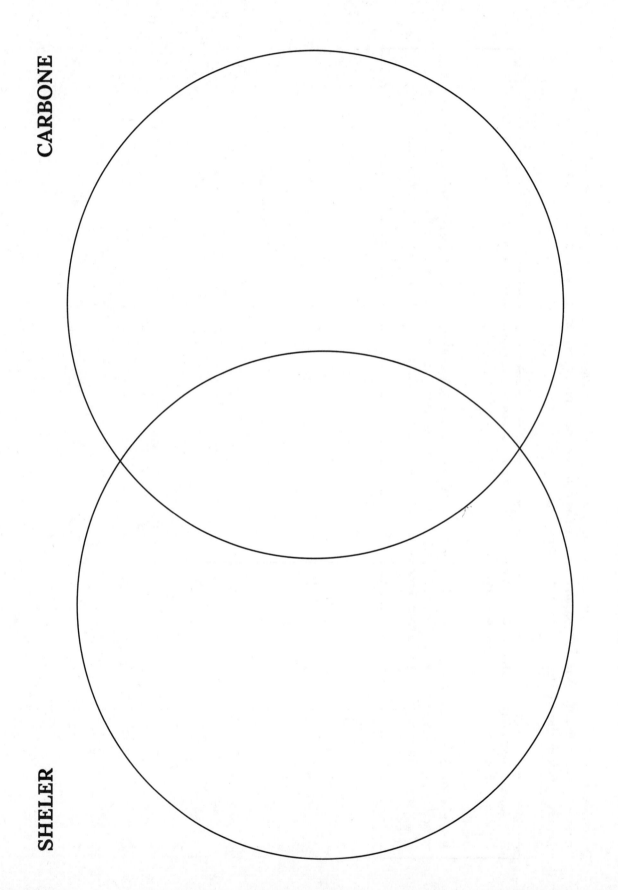

Name _____

Date _____   Class _____

Handout 33A: Presentation Tracker

Directions: Use this table to take notes on the poster presentations you visited.

Presenter Names	Topic	Findings	Connection to Jamestown's Development and Decline (if applicable)

Name _____

Date _____ Class _____

Handout 34A: End-of-Module Task Resources

Directions: Follow the steps described in the table below and use the noted resources as directed to complete the End-of-Module Task.

	End-of-Module Task Process		
Step	**Step Description**	**Resources** (items in bold are included in this packet)	**√ When Complete**
1	**GET CLEAR** • Understand the End-of-Module Task. • Deconstruct exemplar for the claim, reasons, evidence, and elaboration.	• Assessment 34A • **Exemplar Argument Essay** • **Deconstruct Exemplar Argument**	
2	**PLAN** • Review evidence. • Generate claim. • Plan the reasons and evidence to support your claim. • Take notes about how you will elaborate on your evidence. • Confer with your peers and teacher as needed.	• All of the above • Factor Tracker (Handout 5A and in Response Journals) • Argument Essay Graphic Organizer (Handout 15A)	
3	**DRAFT** • Draft your essay. • Confer with your peers and teacher as needed.	• All of the above	
4	**REVIEW** • Complete Peer Review.	• **Content Review** • **Style and Conventions Editing**	
5	**REVISE** • Review and discuss feedback. • Consult with your peers and teacher as needed. • Revise the structure, content, and language of your essay.	• All of the above	
6	**SELF-ASSESS** • Review Rubric • Complete Self Checklist	• **Argument Writing Checklist** • Argument Writing Rubric	
7	**SUBMIT** • Make final revisions. • Submit your essay. • You're done! ·		

Name _____

Date _____   Class _____

Exemplar Argument Essay

Prompt: Write an essay in which you argue whether the social factors or environmental factors were the cause JR1225B's death in Jamestown, using evidence from Written in Bone.

The text Written in Bone by Sally Walker describes the work scientists did to learn more about the early settlement of Jamestown, Virginia. They studied the bones of a teenager who died in the early years of the settlement. They named him JR1225B, and tried to figure out what factors might have caused his death. They looked at several factors, both social and environmental.

What do we mean by the terms "social and environmental factors"? Social factors are causes that come from people. They include how people treat each other and behave towards each other. Environmental factors are causes that come from the natural world. They are not made by humans; environmental factors exist in nature.

In Jamestown, this teenager's death could have been caused by a combination of social factors and environmental factors. Based on the evidence they examined, scientists claim that the most important factors in the young man's death in Jamestown were environmental. Although a social factor also mattered, the teenager's wound from an Indian attack, scientists believe that the environmental factors were more important. The most important reasons for their claim are that the teen had poor nutrition, and he was very sick from an infection.

The first reason scientists make this claim is that the young man had suffered from poor nutrition. He had probably not had enough food to eat and not enough iron in the food he did eat. In the text, we read that the "bones above his eye sockets had small holes, a sign that his diet lacked sufficient iron" (Walker 39). In addition, the author writes, "X-rays of the boy's leg bones showed bands called Harris lines, which form when the growth of a bone repeatedly stops and restarts" (Walker 39). This also comes from bad nutrition. Food is an environmental factor, and this young boy did not have enough of the right food. This would make him weaker and more likely to get sick or even to die. So not having good food was a big environmental factor in this teenager's death.

The second reason that scientists make the claim that environmental factors caused the young man's death is that he had a very severe infection in his jaw. They could see that he had had an abscess at the root of one of his teeth. They could tell from his skeleton that the abscess had spread into his chin and jaw and caused an infection. Walker writes, "Depending on the type of bacteria involved, the severity of JR1225B's infection would have soon caused him to die" (Walker 40). Bacteria are an environmental factor. This teenager did not live in a time when there were medicines to treat the bacteria, so the infection in his jaw from that bacteria killed him. This was a major environmental factor in his death.

To conclude, scientists who have studied the young man's skeleton have decided that the evidence for environmental factors in his death is very strong. If he had had better food, and had not been so sick from an infection, he may have lived longer. It's important to recognize the power of environmental factors in trying to understand how events turn out as they do.

Name _____

Date _____ Class _____

Step 1: Deconstruct Exemplar Argument Essay

Claim

Reason

Evidence

Reason

Evidence

Name _____

Date _____ Class _____

Step 4: Peer Review

Content Review	
Writer of Essay	**Reviewer of Essay**
1. Does the **INTRODUCTION** contain a **hook**? An **introduction** to the topic and task? A **claim**? A preview of the **supporting reasons**? Underline and label each part of the introduction on the draft. How could the introduction be improved?	
2. Does **EACH SUPPORTING PARAGRAPH** have a **reason**? Circle the reason in each paragraph. Is it clear how this reason supports the claim? How could it support the claim better?	

Name _____

Date _____ Class _____

3. Is textual evidence included and cited in **EACH SUPPORTING PARAGRAPH**? Is the evidence relevant? Does it support the reason? How could it be improved?

4. Does **EACH SUPPORTING PARAGRAPH** provide thorough elaboration of the evidence provided? Underline where you see elaboration. How could it be improved? Overall, does this paragraph support the writer's claim? How could it be improved?

Name _____

Date _____ Class _____

5. Is there a **CONCLUDING** paragraph? Does it contain the "So What"? How could the conclusion be improved?

Name

Date   Class

Style and Conventions Editing		
	Yes	No
1. Are all pronouns in the correct case (subjective, objective, or possessive)?		
How could this be improved?		
2. Are there any inappropriate shifts in pronoun number or person?		
How could this be improved?		
3. Are there a variety of sentence patterns?		
How could this be improved?		
4. How effectively does the narrative follow the **conventions** of standard written English? Note where you see convention, spelling, punctuation, or grammar errors.		

Name _____

Date _____ Class _____

Step 6: Argument Writing Checklist

	Self +/ Δ	Peer +/ Δ	Teacher +/ Δ
Structure			
I respond to all parts of the prompt.			
I focus on my argument throughout the piece.			
I introduce the claim clearly in my introduction paragraph.			
My introduction paragraph gives some kind of preview of the rest of the piece.			
I organize my reasons and evidence clearly in body paragraphs.			
My conclusion paragraph supports and expands on the focus.			
I use transitions to smoothly and logically connect paragraphs and ideas.			
Development			
I support my claim with clear reasons and sufficient evidence from at least two texts.			
My evidence is accurate and relevant to the claim.			
I elaborate upon evidence by analyzing it accurately.			
Style			
I use a variety of sentence patterns (simple, compound, complex, compound-complex) to add clarity and interest to my writing.			
I use vocabulary words that are specific and appropriate to the content.			
I write precisely and concisely, without using unnecessary words.			
I write in an appropriately formal style.			
My writing style is appropriate for the audience.			
Conventions			
All of my sentences are complete. (no fragments)			
I avoid informal language such as slang.			
Total # of +'s			

Volume of Reading Reflection Questions

Narrating the Unknown, Grade 6, Module 3

Student Name: _____

Text: _____

Author: _____

Topic: _____

_____

Genre/type of book: _____

Directions: Share your knowledge about Jamestown, early settlements, or anthropology by answering the questions below.

Informational Text:

1. **Wonder:** What drew you to read this informational text? Cite three things you noticed or wondered as you first oriented to the book.

2. **Organize:** Summarize a central idea of the text and its supporting details, including details about things that happened long ago.

3. **Reveal:** Choose a key individual, event, or idea in the text. Describe how the author elaborated on it with details in the text or illustrations.

4. **Distill:** What is the most important insight you gained from this text?

5. **Know:** How does this text's presentation of information compare and contrast with another text on a similar topic?

6. **Vocabulary**: Write and define three important vocabulary words that you learned in this text. In what kind of discussions might you use each word?

Literary Text:

1. **Wonder**: After reading the first few pages of the text, what inferences can you draw?

2. **Organize**: Write a short summary of the story including the main character(s), setting, conflict, and resolution.

3. **Reveal**: Describe how a main character in the story changes as the plot moves toward resolution.

4. **Distill**: What is a theme of this story? How do particular details convey that theme?

5. **Know**: What have you learned about the world through this piece of (historical) fiction?

6. **Vocabulary**: Identify three words that the author used to shape the tone in this text. Explain the effect of the word use in context.

Wit & Wisdom Parent Tip Sheet

WHAT IS MY GRADE 6 STUDENT LEARNING IN MODULE 3?

Wit & Wisdom is our English curriculum. It builds knowledge of key topics in history, science, and literature through the study of excellent texts. By reading and responding to literature and nonfiction texts, we will build knowledge of the following topics:

Module 1: Resilience in the Great Depression

Module 2: A Hero's Journey

Module 3: Narrating the Unknown

Module 4: Courage in Crisis

In the third module, *Narrating the Unknown*, students work across multiple texts and genres to construct a complex picture of life and struggle in Jamestown, assessing the forces—both internal and external—that brought the near demise of the colony. We will ask the question: *How did the social and environmental challenges in the unknown world of Jamestown shape its development and decline?*

OUR CLASS WILL READ THESE TEXTS:

Historical Fiction Novel (Literary)

- *Blood on the River: Jamestown 1607*, Elisa Carbone

Scientific Account (Informational)

- *Written in Bone: Buried Lives of Jamestown and Colonial Maryland*, Sally Walker

OUR CLASS WILL EXAMINE THESE PAINTINGS:

- *Nighthawks*, Edward Hopper
- *The Lighthouse at Two Lights*, Edward Hopper
- *Lighthouse Hill*, Edward Hopper

OUR CLASS WILL READ THIS ARTICLE:

- "Rethinking Jamestown," Jeffery Sheler

OUR CLASS WILL READ AND LISTEN TO THIS SPEECH:

- "Address to Captain John Smith," Chief Powhatan

OUR CLASS WILL VIEW THIS VIDEO:

- "Innovation in Plain Sight," Amy Herman

OUR CLASS WILL ASK THESE QUESTIONS:

- How do the settlers respond to the challenges of their journey to the unknown?
- Who has the greatest impact on Samuel's development during his time in Jamestown?
- How do the settlers' and the Powhatans' responses to the challenges of Jamestown impact its development and decline?
- How does the art and science of observation contribute to a more complete narrative of Jamestown's development and decline?
- How did the social and environmental factors in the unknown world of Jamestown shape its development and decline?

QUESTIONS TO ASK AT HOME:

As your Grade 6 student reads, ask:

- *What is the essential meaning, or most important message, in this book?*

BOOKS TO READ AT HOME:

- *Every Bone Tells a Story: Hominin Discoveries, Deductions and Debates,* Jill Rubalcaba and Peter Robertshaw
- *The Sign of the Beaver,* Elizabeth George Speare
- *The Lost Colony of Roanoke,* Jean Fritz
- *Amelia Lost: The Life and Disappearance of Amelia Earhart,* Candace Fleming
- *Emperor's Silent Army: Terracotta Warriors of Ancient China,* Jane O'Connor
- *1607: A New Look at Jamestown,* Karen Lange

IDEAS FOR TALKING ABOUT EVENTS OF THE PAST:

Search together online for "history mysteries" such as Roanoke Settlement, Stonehenge, or Lost City of Atlantis. Ask:

- *What happened?*
- *What are some ways historians and writers make sense of the past?*

CREDITS

Great Minds® has made every effort to obtain permission for the reprinting of all copyrighted material. If any owner of copyrighted material is not acknowledged herein, please contact Great Minds® for proper acknowledgment in all future editions and reprints of this module.

- All material from the *Common Core State Standards for English Language Arts & Literacy in History/Social Studies, Science, and Technical Subjects* © Copyright 2010 National Governors Association Center for Best Practices and Council of Chief State School Officers. All rights reserved.

- All images are used under license from Shutterstock.com unless otherwise noted.

- For updated credit information, please visit **http://witeng.link/credits**.

ACKNOWLEDGMENTS

Great Minds® Staff

The following writers, editors, reviewers, and support staff contributed to the development of this curriculum.

Ann Brigham, Lauren Chapalee, Sara Clarke, Emily Climer, Lorraine Griffith, Emily Gula, Sarah Henchey, Trish Huerster, Stephanie Kane-Mainier, Lior Klirs, Liz Manolis, Andrea Minich, Lynne Munson, Marya Myers, Rachel Rooney, Aaron Schifrin, Danielle Shylit, Rachel Stack, Sarah Turnage, Michelle Warner, Amy Wierzbicki, Margaret Wilson, and Sarah Woodard.

Colleagues and Contributors

We are grateful for the many educators, writers, and subject-matter experts who made this program possible.

David Abel, Robin Agurkis, Elizabeth Bailey, Julianne Barto, Amy Benjamin, Andrew Biemiller, Charlotte Boucher, Sheila Byrd-Carmichael, Eric Carey, Jessica Carloni, Janine Cody, Rebecca Cohen, Elaine Collins, Tequila Cornelious, Beverly Davis, Matt Davis, Thomas Easterling, Jeanette Edelstein, Kristy Ellis, Moira Clarkin Evans, Charles Fischer, Marty Gephart, Kath Gibbs, Natalie Goldstein, Christina Gonzalez, Mamie Goodson, Nora Graham, Lindsay Griffith, Brenna Haffner, Joanna Hawkins, Elizabeth Haydel, Steve Hettleman, Cara Hoppe, Ashley Hymel, Carol Jago, Jennifer Johnson, Mason Judy, Gail Kearns, Shelly Knupp, Sarah Kushner, Shannon Last, Suzanne Lauchaire, Diana Leddy, David Liben, Farren Liben, Jennifer Marin, Susannah Maynard, Cathy McGath, Emily McKean, Jane Miller, Rebecca Moore, Cathy Newton, Turi Nilsson, Julie Norris, Galemarie Ola, Michelle Palmieri, Meredith Phillips, Shilpa Raman, Tonya Romayne, Emmet Rosenfeld, Jennifer Ruppel, Mike Russoniello, Deborah Samley, Casey Schultz, Renee Simpson, Rebecca Sklepovich, Amelia Swabb, Kim Taylor, Vicki Taylor, Melissa Thomson, Lindsay Tomlinson, Melissa Vail, Keenan Walsh, Julia Wasson, Lynn Welch, Yvonne Guerrero Welch, Emily Whyte, Lynn Woods, and Rachel Zindler.

Early Adopters

The following early adopters provided invaluable insight and guidance for Wit & Wisdom:

- Bourbonnais School District 53 • Bourbonnais, IL
- Coney Island Prep Middle School • Brooklyn, NY
- Gate City Charter School for the Arts • Merrimack, NH
- Hebrew Academy for Special Children • Brooklyn, NY
- Paris Independent Schools • Paris, KY
- Saydel Community School District • Saydel, IA
- Strive Collegiate Academy • Nashville, TN
- Valiente College Preparatory Charter School • South Gate, CA
- Voyageur Academy • Detroit, MI

Design Direction provided by Alton Creative, Inc.

Project management support, production design and copyediting services provided by **ScribeConcepts.com**

Copyediting services provided by Fine Lines Editing

Product management support provided by Sandhill Consulting